FANTASTIC
WORD
PUZZLES

Michael B. Mager

SCHOLASTIC INC.
New York Toronto London Auckland Sydney

For my parents, Seymour and Frieda Mager

ISBN 0-590-96224-8

Copyright © 1981 by Michael B. Mager.
All rights reserved. Published by Scholastic Inc.

12 11 10 9 8   5 6 7 8/0

HOW TO SOLVE
FANTASTIC WORD PUZZLES

Welcome to the weird, weird world of fantastic word puzzles. These are puzzles which contain a familiar word or phrase in a sort of code. Your assignment, puzzle solver, is to crack the code in each puzzle. To do that, you'll have to look carefully at the arrangement, size, and position of each group of mixed-up letters, words, and symbols.

To solve the puzzles, you must read them exactly as you see them. Here is an example:

WORK
TIME

Notice that the word, "work," is over the word, "time." The answer to this sample puzzle is, "work overtime." Here's another one.

CAJUSTSE

No, this isn't a foreign language, nor is it the bottom line of your doctor's eye chart. If you look closely, you'll find that there are two words mixed together here. The word, "just," is in the word, "case." The answer to this puzzle is, "just in case."

Now that you have the idea, you're ready to tackle the toughies. When you've finished each page, check your answers against those in the back of the book . . . and please, no peeking!

1. cyclecyclecycle

2. hair

3. PRO MISE

4. knbow

5. W.OODS

1

STARS

2

2:30
5:02

3

g
e
trouble

4

VANISHA | R

5

the BecBcc

1. flash³

2. temperature

3. lofallve

4. the morning

5. guard
guard

1	*paid* I'm *worked*
2	**KDI**
3	pant pant
4	8:45 OPERATOR
5	SE SAME

7

1. SM^{GO}OKE

2. mesnackal

3. "ALONG

4. MARINE CREW

5. oror O

1 HICANS

2 i'm fed up

3 DOG
THE

4
HAY
HAY
HAY
HAY
HAY

5 de cision

9

1. *TAKE A* nap

2. hand hand car

3. it doesn't
   +up
   _____

4. DON'T GET YOUR HOPE HOPE

5. SOMEDROPTIME

1

walking hahandnd

2

achancen

3

THE   GREAT

4

behind ball ball ball ball ball ball ball ball

5

DE ful

DOORS

1. umph umph umph

2. scope

3. HRISTMAS TRE

4. £ cake

5. in fuel

1

cmopnya

2

the

NATIONNATION

3

run
sentence

4

stitute
sugar

5

right

1

GER&better

2

T E N
N   G
E   A
M   G
E   E
M   E

3

NI GHT

4

14

STICK 11111

NECK

KILLER

I'M
THE WAY
THERE

smoke
smoke
smoke
smoke
smoke
smoke

1

WOALICENDERLAND

2

counter

3

ooo circus

4

head
head

5

lake
tario

1. case letters

2. the momanon

3. bad sight

4. dangerous

5. PART

1. **busines**

2. I've got my iiii
   you

3. **FOOT FOOT**

4. **tetestrm**

5.
   sign
   line

1. E Y E

2. LOAD

3. visit

4. get it all

5. moon 2

1.

WEIGHT
WEIGHT BOXERS
WEIGHT

2.

COLLEGE°°

3.

cut

4.

CARIBBEAN

5.

the past you

1. *podpodpod*

2. **MATH THE**

3. SCORE A TOUCH

4. *chawhorge*

5. 1234 US

1

STAND YOU
I

2

HOUSE

PRAIRIE

3

dollar   *dollar*

4

ONCE
4:56

5

KN
OT

1.

line sit

(ǝuıן) *(ǝuıן)*

2.

A DANCE²

3.

b
g   o
n   x
i

4.

i√t

5.

CAKE *(inverted)*

1. M1LLION

2.

3.
b
ba
back

4. co**u**ple

5. **line** read line

long
due

error

ENDEND

league

THE **TOP**

1

WHAT MUST

2

ceresswearingmony

3

of way

4

car

5

```
        C
        H
        E
HOT     C EL
        K
```

1. **PU**

2. ~~CHECK~~

3. LOP   LOP

4. BROKE

5. PRICES

27

1. *he get get get get everything*

2. What's going
here

3. **mireadynute**

4. have a good 9:00

5. **shake well using**

STREET

1

2

smoker smoker smoker

3

TIMING TI MING

4

CIRCUITS
LOAD

5

ground railroad
the

6-4 BOARD

sip soda^w
st^{tr}

HE ART
SURGERY

strawberry serves

HAN$_Y$D^O$_U$H^A^{R}$_E$ND

1.

neon

2.

T I MEAT

3.

pe a soup

4.

uP

5.

SNOW
ALL

31

1. **the weather feel**

2. TELL **TALES**

3. p—ease stand

4. *try* *for the team*

5. cover agent

1

BLIND MAY 24

2

ENERGY age

3

Wilson

4

NOTHING IT

5

WAY

SUPER

1

DANE

2

WHAT ARE YOU NOW

3

4

1

STRAWBERRY cake

2

$$\begin{matrix} & S & \\ & K & \\ & I & \\ \text{COUN} & \text{T} & \text{RY} \\ & I & \\ & N & \\ & G & \end{matrix}$$

SKIING
COUNTRY

3

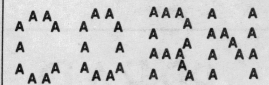

```
  A A        A A         A A A    A         A
A     A    A     A       A    A        A A A     A
A     A    A     A       A A A A  A  A  A  A A A  A
A   A A    A A A A       A    A    A A     A      A
```

4

FATHER

1. **SGGE**

2. *the boom*

3. THE **wake** MORNING

4. NING **BREAD**

5. tide

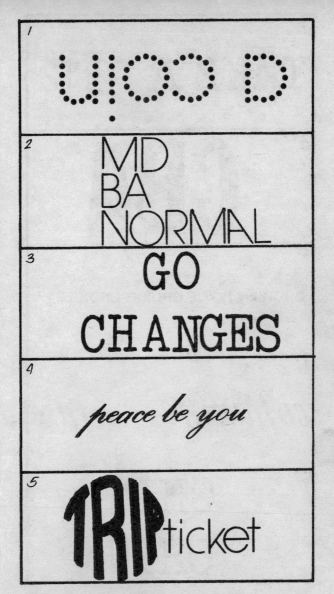

1. U!OO D

2. MD
BA
NORMAL

3. GO
CHANGES

4. *peace be you*

5. TRIPticket

1

TAKE A ꟼƎTƨ

2

GBA

3

CHOICE CHOICE CHOICE CHOICE ?

4

copayme   *tax*

5

CHIN

CHIN

1

6 o'clock
·

2

THAT

3

OOF FEE

4

play stop

5

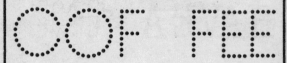

H H club

1. ho

2. ~~hart~~
heart

3. HAVE A TIME

4. *Dried*

5. state highway state

40

1. TRAVEL
   囗囗

2. lfatheraw

3. 'path

4. G HISTORY

5. ✓ ERED FLAG

1

thought have an

2

ruplet
ruplet
ruplet
ruplet

3

NOON THIS

4

memory

5

ju
s
i

SOCIETY

ǝlᴉʇs

speed limit

stay

FELLOW,

the poet

SPACE

1

SUSIAN

2

LOOK YOU LEAP

3

WILLOW WIND WILLOW

4

3:15 & 3:15 again

5

DIAMERICANAN

A **S E T** PERSON

2

SHOW

3

the runway
shoot

STONE

4

choose

5

choose

1.

SUGAR
U
N

2.

drive
w t ay
h
e

3.

I'm tied the moment

4.

mhave faithe

5.

LOOK OUT

1. *dump* **DOWN** *dump*
2. DECISION TURN
3. **play play**
4. SPOT
5. all choked

the earth	the earth
the earth	the earth

2

ATOMIC

FALL

3

GET GRADE GRADE

4

Máte

5

WIRE

ACT

1 **1000000AIRE**

2 SOUTH

3 GEN ERATION

4 SIT PLEASE

5 I'M Your

1. gone wind

2. sitting world

3. you it's just me

4. school diploma

5. NO WAY IT WAY

50

1. **nepainck**

2. **stay**   **me**

3. ***thewindow***

4. **my** **mind**

5.

1. DOOR

2. WISH STAR

3. WALK WALK

4. WORLD THE

5. the glow dark

1. the rules *she*

2. HEAR TED

3. wake dawn

4. ROOT^2

5. FIGHT

1 GUM

2 HABITS

3 GOLF FOOTBALL CAR.

4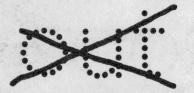

5 HEART TALK HEART

1 ¢ury

2 DOWN

3 hang

4 IS IS IS IS IS IS IS IS IS IS COURT

5 HAR$

1. engine engine airplane

2. L   IP

3. the + e e mountains

4. **BLOW PHOTOS**

5. help the way

1

SKY

BLOWN

2

LOOK⊨

3

bopussots

4

ESCAPE

5

don't rule

me

1

)& conquer

2

222 DAY

3

0
oooo

4

this world
t's

5

RIGHT
9:17

1. watch

2. *way way street*

3. NING **ROD**

4. score
   the   wins

5. **the sky cast**

59

1.

LEAGUES

P L A Y

2.

5:00

3.

the worse

4.

STRONG STRONG STRONG STRONG

W	W	W	W	
h	h	h	h	
e	e	e	e	drive
e	e	e	e	
l	l	l	l	

2

L

R E

E

D A

D

3

Game

4

staircase staircase staircase staircase staircase staircase

1. HOUSE

2. CANYON

3. MORE THAN EYE

4.  ENEMIES

1.

POTATO,

2.

S F
A LOT O
L O

3.

GO
ever
ever
ever
ever

4.

BOMB

1

my you're way

2

```
    e
  eyed
    e
    d
```

3

world, world, world, world...

4

hoacele

5

1 playing *records*

2 BE LEVEL

3 JOURNEY EARTH

4 wear wear long

5 FILLED JACKET

65

1

ON THE ◯ TARGET

2

L
K **you** O
O

3

electrical

4

go
board

5

take ⟶ take

let

1

SAND$

2

adpayvance

3

WORK

4

1,2,3,4 Dracula

5

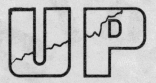

IT

1 THE RULES

2 WIT

3 OFFICE

4 rain

1.

A BASKET

2.

pl STUDY BE AN ay

3.

NEFOR TU (arranged in circle: TUNE FOR)

4.

TROMY EARSUBLE I'M

1. DIGARYANA

2. W

   ~~K~~aste

3. **friendfriend**

4. *IT'S A* world

5. innocent STANDER
              STANDER

1. **somewhere the rainbow**

2. **I'M YOU**

3. **GO datedate**

4. **dont gett mee**

5. **SPEAK**

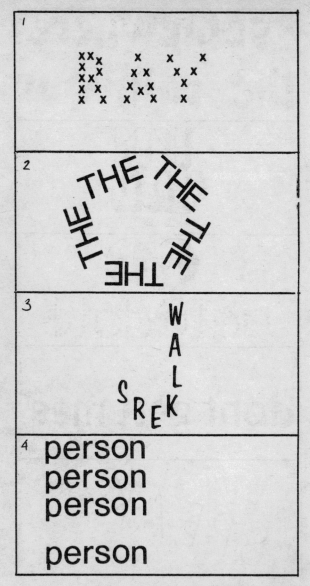

1

swear

BIBLE

BIBLE

BIBLE

BIBLE

BIBLE

2

T
HE
BER
MUDA

3

babes

4

MAN

1

ICE^3

2

CLAS   SES

3

4

O

11/3/46

H   W

5

odd
odd US

74

1. RELAX
WEEK

2. * FISH

3. **HEET**

4. PIG   PIG   PIG

5. apple

1 *chair*

2 # DEAL

3 ## the all family

4 st ste steam

5 MONEY

1. *heels wear*

2. my rope I'm

3. SKATE ice

4. RAEG

5. $\dfrac{horse}{4}$

1.

2. *pressure*
   work

3. INFORGETMATION

4. DOOR SALESMAN DOOR

5. BIG HORN

1.
```
        W
k  clock  o
        r
        I
```

2.
slept (with large **I** above)

3. RACE TIME (TIME inverted/upside down)

4. *have* *a* chance

5. PAINS

1 **TURN THE TV**
2 **the jack box**
3 HARD X ARE COMING
4 SCHOOL
5 **your shirt is no**

DROP

1

ORDINARY ORDINARY PERFORMANCE

2

perso **nality**

3

knock you enter

4

 **TRUE**

5

it took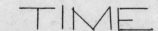

1 CHANCE

THE OTHER

2 ONE GO EAR &

3 I'm
come *happiness*

4 orders I was only

5 *Wear*
All   All

1

GRAPE

2

dirty crosser crosser

3

play it ear

4

you can't have it
you can't have it

5

**be
lookout**

ANSWERS

Page 4
1. tricycle
2. curly hair
3. broken promise
4. be in the know
5. lost in the woods

Page 5
1. falling stars
2. Times Square
3. get into trouble
4. vanish into thin air
5. the seven seas

Page 6
1. flash cube
2. rising temperature
3. fall in love
4. top of the morning
5. crossing guards

Page 7
1. I'm underpaid and overworked.
2. mixed-up kid
3. pair of pants
4. big-time operator
5. open sesame

Page 8
1. go up in smoke
2. in between-meal snack
3. inch along
4. submarine crew
5. double or nothing

Page 9
1. *The Last of the Mohicans*
2. I'm fed up.
3. the underdog
4. haystack
5. split decision

Page 10
1. take a short nap
2. secondhand car
3. It doesn't add up.
4. Don't get your hopes up.
5. Drop in sometime.

Page 11
1. walking hand-in-hand
2. an outside chance
3. the great outdoors
4. behind the 8-ball
5. delightful

Page 12
1. triumph
2. microscope
3. trim a Christmas tree
4. pound cake
5. low in fuel

Page 13
1. mixed company
2. the United Nations
3. run-on sentence
4. sugar substitute
5. right on cue

Page 14
1. bigger and better
2. engagement ring
3. night shift
4. wisecracks

Page 15
1. stick one's neck out
2. giant killer
3. I'm on my way over there.
4. smokestack

Page 16
1. *Alice in Wonderland*
2. check-out counter
3. three-ring circus
4. Two heads are better than one.
5. Lake Ontario

Page 17
1. lower case letters
2. the man in the moon
3. bad oversight
4. dangerous curve
5. bit part

Page 18
1. unfinished business
2. I've got my eyes on you.
3. flat feet
4. midterm test
5. Sign on the dotted line.

Page 19
1. eye-drops
2. heavy load
3. short visit
4. get away from it all
5. half moon

Page 20
1. middleweight boxers
2. college degrees
3. short cut
4. Caribbean Sea
5. Put the past behind you.

Page 21
1. tripod
2. the aftermath
3. score a touchdown
4. Who is in charge?
5. Count on us.

Page 22
1. I understand you.
2. *Little House on the Prairie*
3. change of a dollar
4. once upon a time
5. square knot

Page 23
1. sit on the sidelines
2. a square dance
3. boxing ring
4. check into it
5. upside-down cake

Page 24
1. one in a million
2. wise guys
3. quarterback, halfback, fullback
4. *The Odd Couple*
5. Read between the lines.

Page 25
1. long overdue
2. margin of error
3. end to end
4. little league
5. the big top

Page 26
1. What goes up must come down.
2. swearing-in ceremony
3. right of way
4. compact car
5. check into a hotel

Page 27
1. mixed-up
2. cancelled check
3. lopsided
4. flat broke
5. reduced prices

Page 28
1. He forgets everything.
2. What's going on here?
3. ready in a minute
4. Have a good time.
5. Shake well before using.

Page 29
1. street corner
2. chain smoker
3. split-second timing
4. overloaded circuits
5. the underground
   railroad

Page 30
1. scoreboard
2. sip soda through
   a straw
3. open-heart surgery
4. strawberry preserves
5. You are in good hands.

Page 31
1. neon light
2. take it lying down
3. split-pea soup
4. fatten up
5. all covered with snow

Page 32
1. feel under the weather
2. tell tall tales
3. Please stand in line.
4. try out for the team
5. undercover agent

Page 33
1. blind date
2. energy shortage
3. Flip Wilson
4. nothing to it
5. super highway

Page 34
1. Great Dane
2. What are you up to
   now?
3. diamond necklace
4. merry-go-round

Page 35
1. strawberry shortcake
2. cross-country skiing
3. acorn
4. stepfather

Page 36
1. scrambled eggs
2. lower the boom
3. wake up in the morning
4. shortnin' bread
5. low tide

Page 37
1. flip a coin
2. two degrees above normal
3. undergo changes
4. Peace be with you.
5. round-trip ticket

Page 38
1. take a step backwards
2. mixed bag
3. multiple-choice question
4. pay income tax
5. double chin

Page 39
1. six o'clock on the dot
2. fancy that
3. coffee break
4. play shortstop
5. 4-H club

Page 40
1. high ho
2. change of heart
3. have a rough time
4. dried up
5. interstate highway

Page 41
1. travel overseas
2. father-in-law
3. footpath
4. go down in history
5. checkered flag

Page 42
1. have an afterthought
2. quadruplets
3. this afternoon
4. short memory
5. just around the corner

Page 43
1. high society
2. turnstile
3. outer space
4. stay under the speed limit
5. Longfellow, the poet

Page 44

1. black-eyed Susan
2. Look before you leap.
3. *The Wind in the Willows*
4. time and time again
5. American Indian

Page 45

1. a heavyset person
2. sideshow
3. overshoot the runway
4. cornerstone
5. choose sides

Page 46

1. run out of sugar
2. drive on the throughway
3. I'm tied up at the moment.
4. Have faith in me.
5. Look out below!

Page 47

1. down in the dumps
2. overturn a decision
3. double play
4. spotlight
5. all choked up

Page 48

1. the four corners of the earth
2. atomic fallout
3. get bad grades
4. checkmate
5. high wire act

Page 49

1. millionaire
2. down south
3. generation gap
4. Sit down, please.
5. I'm on your side.

Page 50

1. *Gone With the Wind*
2. sitting on top of the world
3. It's just between you and me.
4. high school diploma
5. no two ways about it

Page 51

1. pain in the neck
2. Stay away from me.
3. Close the window.
4. It crossed my mind.
5. pay by check

Page 52
1. open door
2. wish upon a star
3. sidewalks
4. the underworld
5. glow in the dark

Page 53
1. She follows the rules.
2. brokenhearted
3. wake up at dawn
4. square root
5. uphill fight

Page 54
1. gum drop
2. bad habits
3. sports car
4. cancelled out
5. heart-to-heart talk

Page 55
1. turn of the century
2. slim down
3. hang-up
4. tennis court
5. harmony

Page 56
1. twin-engine airplane
2. split lip
3. the Andes Mountains
4. blow-up photos
5. Help is on the way.

Page 57
1. blown sky high
2. Look it up.
3. *Puss in Boots*
4. narrow escape
5. Don't rule me out.

Page 58
1. divide and conquer
2. Tuesday
3. four degrees below zero
4. It's out of this world.
5. right on time

Page 59
1. watch out
2. two-way street
3. lightning rod
4. the high score wins
5. The sky is overcast.

Page 60
1. play in the big leagues
2. five o'clock shadow
3. a turn for the worse
4. strong box

Page 61
1. four-wheel drive
2. ringleader
3. tied game
4. spiral staircases

Page 62
1. roundhouse
2. Grand Canyon
3. more than meets
   the eyes
4. archenemies

Page 63
1. potato chip
2. fools around a lot
3. go on forever
4. H-bomb

Page 64
1. You're in my way.
2. cross-eyed
3. World Series
4. ace in the hole
5. Broadway

Page 65
1. long-playing records
2. be on the level
3. *A Journey to the
   Center of the Earth*
4. wear long underwear
5. down-filled jacket

Page 66
1. zero in on the target
2. look around you
3. electrical outlet
4. go overboard
5. take sides

Page 67
1. sand dollar
2. pay in advance
3. work it out
4. Count Dracula
5. crack up

Page 68
1. bend the rules
2. halfwit
3. branch office
4. rainbow

Page 69
1. sink a basket
2. be an understudy in a play
3. wheel of fortune
4. I'm up to my ears in trouble.

Page 70
1. Gary, Indiana
2. Haste makes waste.
3. close friends
4. It's a small world.
5. innocent bystanders

Page 71
1. "Somewhere Over the Rainbow"
2. I'm stuck on you.
3. go on a double date
4. Don't get me wrong.
5. speak up

Page 72
1. x-ray
2. the Pentagon
3. jaywalkers
4. missing person

Page 73
1. swear on a stack of bibles
2. the Bermuda Triangle
3. baseball diamond
4. Batman

Page 74
1. ice cube
2. cut classes
3. be careful
4. How about a date?
5. The odds are against us.

Page 75
1. Relax on the weekend.
2. starfish
3. bad heat spell
4. three little pigs
5. apple turnover

Page 76
1. high chair
2. big deal
3. *All in the Family*
4. build up steam
5. raise money

Page 77
1. wear high heels
2. I'm at the end of my rope.
3. skate on thin ice
4. reverse gear
5. quarter horse

Page 78
1. bottomless pit
2. work under pressure
3. get inside information
4. door-to-door salesman
5. Little Big Horn

Page 79
1. work around the clock
2. I overslept.
3. race against time
4. have a slim chance
5. growing pains

Page 80
1. Turn on the TV.
2. jack-in-the-box
3. Hard times are coming.
4. high school dropout
5. Your shirt is on backwards.

Page 81
1. extraordinary performance
2. split personality
3. Knock before you enter.
4. true beyond a shadow of doubt
5. It took a long time.

Page 82
1. fat chance
2. go in one ear and out the other
3. I'm overcome with happiness.
4. I was only following orders.
5. wear overalls

Page 83
1. grape jam
2. dirty double crosser
3. play it by ear
4. You can't have it both ways.
5. be on the lookout